SIBYLS

Roman sesterce depicting the profile image of a Sibyl.
Minted circa 65 BCE under Lucius Manlius Torquatus.

(Ashmolean Museum, Oxford.)